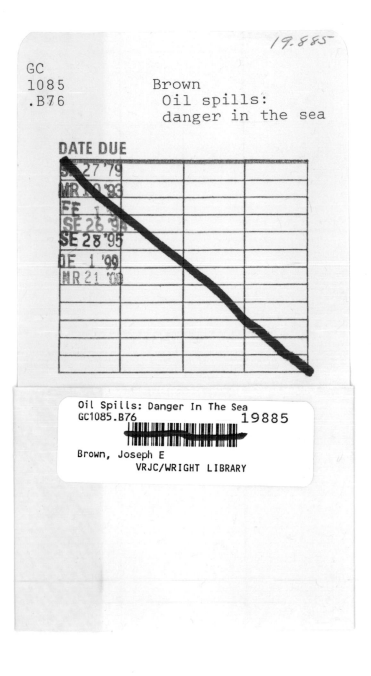

OIL SPILLS

Danger in the Sea

OIL SPILLS
Danger in the Sea

Joseph E. Brown
Illustrated with photographs

DODD, MEAD & COMPANY / New York

1 2 3 4 5 6 7 8 9 10

Library of Congress Cataloging in Publication Data

Brown, Joseph E   1929-
    Oil spills.

    Includes index.
    1. Oil spills.   2.   Oil spills and wildlife.
I. Title.
GC1085.B76   363.6   78-7743
ISBN 0-396-07607-6

For Mark

Contents

OIL SPILLS

Danger in the Sea

1

OIL IN THE SEA

Late in the evening of August 9, 1974, the tanker *Metula,* bound from Saudi Arabia for the Chilean port of Quintero Bay, ran aground on a patch of shoals in the Strait of Magellan near the tip of South America. The site was not many miles from Cape Horn, dreaded by mariners since the days of sailing ships for the tumultuous storms, heavy winds, and swift ocean currents that make navigation difficult and dangerous.

The *Metula* was a huge ship, one of the largest afloat in the world at the time. She was 1,067 feet long, longer than three football fields. Her draft—the distance from waterline to keel —was 62 feet, higher than a six-story building. Her registered deadweight tonnage (or DWT) was 206,000 tons. Because the tonnage exceeded 200,000, the *Metula* was in fact one of the first liquid cargo-carrying vessels to be designated a *super*tanker, or, more technically, a VLCC, *very large crude carrier.*

A tug assists the tanker Metula *after grounding in Strait of Magellan, August 9, 1974.*

A subsequent investigation failed to determine clearly why the *Metula* had veered off course and gone aground. However, strong currents and tidal flow in the Strait of Magellan were cited as probable causes. A minimum of navigation aids was also considered. Perhaps adequate for other parts of the ocean, they may have been insufficient for this dangerous area.

Regardless of the cause, the grounding marked the beginning of a calamity of major proportions.

For hours, the *Metula*'s captain tried desperately to free his vessel from the rocks. Even the energy of her engines running full speed astern, however, was insufficient, and on the second day—August 10—strong currents swung the helpless ship to starboard. The movement tore open a gaping hole in the hull, and water began flooding the ship's engine compartments.

Alerted by radio, the U.S. Coast Guard airlifted several pumps to the scene, and lowered them by helicopter to the ship. As his crew tried to refloat the vessel, the captain thought of his cargo: 196,000 tons of light Arabian crude oil, which now had begun oozing from the hull fissure into the Atlantic Ocean. For several days oil flowed out—53,000 tons of it, or nearly one-fourth of the total cargo.

Because Coast Guard salvors mistakenly believed that the oil would drift into the open ocean and dissipate, no attempt was made to clean up the oil slick. The site was extremely remote; airlifting the necessary cleanup manpower there in time might have been impossible anyway. Shifting winds and currents carried the oil instead in the opposite direction, toward the South American shoreline, a mile away. Within hours, it began smearing the coast, eventually to cover fifty miles of coastline.

The oil congealed into brownish lumps, which scientists nickname "mousse," and smothered countless marine organisms. It

Pumps are put in place in an attempt to transfer oil from stranded Metula *to smaller tanker* Harvella.

made rocks so slippery that limpets (small cone-shaped organisms which live attached to rocks) could not survive.

Seabirds were the slick's most pathetic victims. About two hundred were found dead or dying, becoming immobilized as they waded, swam, or dived through the oil. Particularly vulnerable were cormorants; fish-feeders, they were "captured" by the oil as they dived through it for food.

Other birds affected were penguins, terns, albatrosses, and ducks. Only the chance timing of the *Metula*'s grounding prevented an even greater loss. In mid-September, tens of thousands of penguins migrate from the Antarctic to Chile's Los

Penguinos National Park, an important bird refuge. Had the accident occurred a month later, some scientists have speculated, the oil slick may have meant possible extinction of an entire species of this aquatic bird.

The effect of the slick was first observed a few days later by Dr. Roy W. Hann, Jr., a scientist with Texas A&M University, who had been retained as a scientific advisor by the Coast Guard. Dr. Hann returned to the scene the following January, five months after the accident, and again three years later.

He found that while the tides and currents eventually had carried most of the oil away, the accident's aftermath was long-lasting. Populations of marine life recovered in time, but the visible mess of blackened shoreline remained.

"My guess," Dr. Hann reported after his last visit, "is that

Oil spills may adversely affect the fish population.

major effects of the spill will be visible there twenty years from now. The place still looks desolate, and fresh, soft pools of oil lie in the flats [of nearby estuaries]."

The *Metula* incident is symptomatic of an increasingly complex international problem: oil spills in the marine environment.

Every year, according to the U.S. Environmental Protection Agency, more than ten thousand spills occur in United States' waters alone. Only a few are classified as major spills, such as that involving the *Metula*. In terms of the total oil introduced into the marine environment from all sources, major spills are in fact miniscule offenders. Of more than twenty thousand offshore wells drilled along American coastlines, for instance, only three resulted in spill accidents classified as major. But because of the suddenness and dramatic magnitude of their occurrence, they help call attention to a problem which is increasing year by year as the world's demand for fossil fuel sources of energy increases.

Oil spills not only befoul our harbors, bays, estuaries, and oceans, they also adversely affect marine organisms, and endanger, at least temporarily, the supply of seafood products. They threaten human health and safety, and waste precious natural resources.

They are also costly to clean up. A single, 500,000-gallon spill in the St. Lawrence River involving a barge accident is typical; it cost $8 million to clean up. Some spill cleanups cost as high as $1,100 per barrel of oil, many times the commercial value. (An oil "barrel" is forty-two gallons. The odd amount stems from the days when oil was transported in wagons in open wooden casks. Some of the oil was lost by sloshing around; thus the barrels were made in 42-gallon sizes so that at least

19

Tanker Sansinena *spilled almost 20,000 gallons of bunker oil when she exploded at a dock in the Los Angeles Harbor.*

forty gallons, a more easily accountable figure, would be de-livered.)

Not all oil spills are highly damaging. As will be explained in detail later, the effect of any particular spill depends upon many factors: the type and amount of oil lost, the physical characteristics of the area where it is spilled, tides and currents, the weather, how quickly the spill can be detected and cleaned up.

But in every spill there is *some* loss, even if it is merely an unsightly mess to be cleaned up. Depending upon the chemical makeup, oil varies in toxicity. Added suddenly to existing stresses in the ocean environment, spilled oil can have varied effects.

Fish or other organisms may not die, but instead may lose their ability to feed, find shelter, or protect themselves from predators. In an experiment involving deliberately spilled oil, Joseph M. Forms of the Westinghouse Research Laboratory found, for instance, that oil hastens the process by which larval lobsters acquire their familiar reddish color. In their natural growth cycle, lobsters do not "turn red" until they are old enough to cope with predators. By losing their infantile drab-ness too soon, Forms found, they were unable to defend them-selves.

How much oil is spilled in the sea each year? There is no exact answer but a number of scientists have offered estimates based on detailed studies of sources.

According to a study sponsored by the National Academy of Sciences, about 6.113 million metric tons of petroleum hydro-carbons enter the ocean worldwide each year from all sources. (A metric ton is a measure of weight equal to 2,204.62 pounds, or slightly more than the more commonly used ton of 2,000 pounds avoirdupois.)

22

Marine Transport Mode

The largest single source—about one-third—is what the Coast Guard (charged with oil spill law enforcement) calls the *marine transport mode*. This includes all means by which oil is transported at sea: ships, barges, marine pipelines.

The supertanker *Metula* was one such example, as was the tanker *Torrey Canyon*, which ran aground off the coast of England in 1967, spilled 540,000 barrels of oil, and accelerated public demands for spill control.

Transport *accidents*, however, are only a small part of the marine transport mode problem. Accidents such as those involving the *Metula* and *Torrey Canyon*, in fact, account for only about 5 percent of the 2.133 million metric tons of petroleum hydrocarbons introduced during transport.

The other 95 percent of transport oil pollution occurs during routine operations, when tanks of tankers are flushed of oil residue, for instance, or in spillage during transfer of oil to or from a tanker, or from other operational, nonaccidental causes.

Oil tankers are very costly ships to operate. They are only profitable to their owners or charterers when fully in use. If they are being operated at sea empty of cargo, they are not serving their profit-making purpose. However, a shipping company is not always able to arrange for a cargo of oil to carry on a return voyage to replace one that has just been unloaded.

One way that companies can offset this is to transport non-oil cargoes to a home port after delivering oil. To do so, the tanks, which carry a thin residue of oil, must be flushed so that the new cargo will not be contaminated. And even if a tanker carries no cargo, it must carry ballast—usually water— so that it will maintain stability at sea. Once again, the oil residue in cargo tanks must be cleaned out before the ballast is pumped in.

23

Tank cleaning and deballasting of tankers are closely regulated by law. It is illegal, for instance, to pump intentionally any oily waste into any body of water under American jurisdiction. The Coast Guard is responsible for enforcement of this federal law. Technically, the rule applies even to operators of pleasure boats. A "Sunday sailor" who deliberately empties oil or gasoline from an outboard motor is violating the law, and is contributing his tiny share to the overall pollution problem.

The Coast Guard is concerned mostly with major violators, however, and considering the size of today's oil tankers, even one occurrence of deliberate pollution can add substantially to the loss of sea life.

One example may best illustrate this. In July, 1975, residents of a thirty-mile section of the Florida Keys were alarmed to see an oil slick drifting toward their islands. The Keys are a chain of islands which extend into the Caribbean Sea from the Florida mainland.

No source could be seen, but the spill turned out to be a "major" one. It took three weeks to clean up, at a cost of more than $350,000 and 3,215 man-hours of labor.

Scientists investigated the damage. Although natural sea grass acted as an absorbing agent, soaking up much of the oil before it reached the shoreline, many organisms perished. Shore crabs and fiddler crabs, residents of coastal mangrove thickets, died. So did many echinoderms—organisms such as starfish and sea urchins. Many mangrove trees, vital to the coastal ecosystem, died as a result of being "smothered" by oil, and a local commercial pearl oyster industry was threatened.

There are no offshore oil production platforms near the Florida Keys, no oil refineries, no underwater pipelines that might have leaked.

24

The foredeck of a modern supertanker at sea in the Gulf of Mexico.

A research assistant carries out a forensic analysis of oil spills in the laboratory at the Coast Guard Research & Development Center in Groton, Connecticut.

The investigating Coast Guard, which operates antipollution "Strike Forces" around the country, suspected that the spill might have been caused by a tanker illegally discharging oil while far out at sea, beyond detection range.

A massive investigation followed. Samples of the spilled oil were sent to a Coast Guard research laboratory at Groton, Connecticut, to determine if they could be matched up with other samples of oil on file there. This would give the Coast Guard, which maintains records of the various kinds of oil cargo carried to and from American ports, as well as sailing schedules of all ships, a clue to which vessel might have been involved.

A total of 247 tankers in ports along the Gulf of Mexico were

26

boarded by Strike Force personnel. Their cargoes were sampled. On July 24, as the spill cleanup in the Keys was continuing, suspicion pointed strongly to one such ship then in New Orleans.

Her log indicated she had been traveling from Rotterdam, Holland, to New Orleans, and on July13–15 had passed through the offshore Florida area. The vessel was scheduled to pick up a load of grain in Louisiana for delivery to an East Coast American port. To do so, all traces of oil carried on a previous voyage would have to be removed from her tanks.

Samples of oil from the Florida spill very closely matched the type of oil the ship had been known to carry last. Had the ship's master elected simply to flush the tanks at sea, thus saving the expense of doing so in port? The Coast Guard, now having gathered considerable scientific evidence, believed he had.

Criminal charges were filed against the captain. Had he been convicted, he could have been sentenced to a heavy fine or a term in prison. Later, however, the charges were dismissed when prosecutors were unable to establish that the tanker had been in waters under American jurisdiction at the time of the spill.

Although the ship's master escaped penalty, many other tanker captains who have violated antipollution laws have been punished. The incident also emphasizes how, increasingly, the same kind of determined detective work that is used in other areas of law enforcement is now being applied to the antipollution field.

Marine transport mode spill incidents still account for only about one-third of the total amount of petroleum hydrocarbons introduced into the sea each year. What about the remaining two-thirds?

27

Natural Oil Seeps

About 10 percent, or .6 million metric tons, can never be stopped. This comes from natural, sea-floor oil seeps or fissures. These are the so-called "Mother Nature's Oil Wells" that have been spewing oil into the ocean for millions of years. There are an estimated 190 such seeps worldwide. One of the most noted is located near Coal Oil Point in the Santa Barbara Channel of Southern California, not far from where a major man-made oil spill occurred in 1969.

This Coal Oil Point seep was first noted by an English explorer named Vancouver in 1793. A mile from shore, Vancouver observed a wide oil slick that drifted about with the current. "As far as the eye can see," he jotted in his ship's log, "the sea is covered with a sticky, smelly substance."

Biblical scholars suggest that Noah used natural tar from oil seeps to caulk the seams of his ark. "Greek fire," a weapon that Bronze Age warriors used to sling at their enemies, was actually petroleum skimmed from Middle Eastern waters, and heated to a near boiling point.

Although geologists know what causes oil seeps, and approximately how many there are in the world, they do not know what effect, if any, these have on marine life. Unlike sudden, catastrophic spills that dump many tons of oil on an otherwise unaffected section of the sea, seeps ooze at a fairly steady and measurable rate. Most scientists therefore believe that organisms generally have learned to adjust to their presence.

River Runoff

A large percentage of worldwide marine oil pollution—25 percent—comes from river runoff. All rivers eventually find their way to the sea. As they flow from mountain source to river

Industrial waste being emptied into a creek.

delta and eventually into the ocean, they pick up and carry along silt and other substances. Often, oily matter is included, a total of 1.6 million metric tons of it each year.

Oil Discharges

Two other contributors—10 percent of the total each—are municipal and industrial discharges of oil. These include wastes from factories and cities which, despite increasing legislation to control them, find their way into rivers and later into the sea.

Individually, they may be almost insignificant contributors. A service station mechanic, for instance, who accidentally or intentionally dumps the result of an automobile's oil change into the gutter, may not seem to be a major polluter. And he is not. But the small amount of oil, perhaps only three or four quarts, soon joins other drip-by-drip contaminants and, collectively, they add up to large amounts. Adding municipal and industrial discharges together with river runoff, that means another 2.5 million metric tons of potentially damaging waste dumped into the sea every year.

Rainfall

Another 10 percent is oil which evaporates, then is returned to the ocean via rainfall.

Offshore Production

A final category is oil from offshore oil production. This includes oil both routinely lost in offshore operations and that in rare but massive accidents.

Perhaps surprisingly, these sources account for only about 2 percent of the petroleum in the marine environment, or about .08 million metric tons annually. As mentioned earlier, only a handful of the more than twenty thousand offshore wells drilled

A drilling platform in the Gulf of Mexico.

in the United States have resulted in accidents classified as "major." Though small percentagewise, compared to other pollution sources, they can be extremely damaging. Unlike the effects of sources which contribute oil on a fairly steady basis, and to which most forms of marine life have become accustomed, the major spills strike suddenly and without warning. Unprepared and unwarned, many organisms are wiped out quickly.

In one sense, though, the major offshore well and tanker accidents have perhaps served a beneficial purpose. Because their spewing oil was massive, and because their potential harm was catastrophic, they helped call worldwide attention to the growing problem of spills of all types.

Strict antipollution laws were passed by Congress soon after the Santa Barbara Channel blowout in 1969. The accident to a large extent is credited with bringing about the creation of the Environmental Protection Agency (EPA), which is devoted to coordinating and enforcing antipollution laws. The grounding of the *Torrey Canyon* two years earlier gave impetus to stronger international laws governing tanker operation and safety. It also accelerated engineering standards in tanker design. And while scientists knew very little about the fate and effects of oil in the marine environment at the time of the Santa Barbara spill, they now have an increasingly substantial—but far from complete—file of knowledge.

A basic question remains unanswered, however. *How much oil can man continue to put into the ocean before the damage becomes irreversible?*

Until recently, the oceans and seas were regarded as being too huge to be affected by pollution. After all, they cover more

32

Coast Guard cutter Dependable *assists in cleanup of burning off-shore oil platform in the Gulf of Mexico, December 1, 1970. It took more than four months to extinguish the fire.*

than two-thirds of the earth, 140 million square miles alto-gether. Especially as the earth's dry land became more popu-lated, more crowded, and thus more valuable, man turned to the sea as a place to dump his wastes. The oceans are vast; how could they be harmed?

Through scientific research, we know now that they *can*. Scientists have gathered considerable evidence that, though the oceans are enormous, even the smallest amount of pollution can have its effect. Life in the ocean is complex and closely inter-related. Even the smallest, microscopic organisms are a food source for larger organisms, and to damage one link in the marine "food chain" is to affect another link.

One much publicized example is how the runoff of some agricultural pesticides from the land into the sea has been at least a contributing factor in the decline of some seabird populations. The chemicals apparently do not affect the birds directly. But they do affect fish which the birds eat, and the ingested hydrocarbons in the pesticides in turn thin the shells of eggs laid by the birds. Many eggs are crushed under the weight of incubating birds, and thus many birds fail to hatch.

Pesticides serve man by destroying insects that prey on his food crops. Oil, too, is beneficial by providing human comfort and convenience. It powers generators that illuminate, cool, and warm factories, homes, and schools. Without petroleum there would be no fuel for automobiles; without petrochemical by-products of petroleum, there would be no automobiles, no plastics, no paints, very few of the thousands of items we take for granted today.

But oil supplies around the world are becoming harder to find and more expensive to process. As petroleum reserves on land become depleted, man is turning increasingly to the sea for new sources of energy. About 20 percent of our petroleum is now produced from marine sources of fossil fuels—*finite*, or exhaustible.

Even exploiting the land and marine petroleum areas to their fullest, however, the United States uses far more energy than it produces. More than half of the oil used in the United States today is imported from other countries, mainly those halfway around the world in the Middle East. This places an even greater reliance on ships as a means of transport, and the danger of ocean oil spills increases.

How far marine pollution may continue before the sea is seriously, irrevocably affected is a major concern of governments, scientists, and oil producers as well.

"The ocean may be able to accommodate petroleum hydrocarbon inputs far above those occurring today," noted the National Academy of Sciences in concluding a major study on oil spills and their effect. "On the other hand, the damage level may be within an order of magnitude of present inputs to the sea. Until we can come closer to answering this basic question, it seems wisest to continue our efforts in the international control of inputs and to push forward research to reduce our current level of uncertainty."

More simply stated, that means that man should attempt to understand the problems of oil spills better—and do something about them—before it is too late.

2

ENERGY FROM THE SEA

Millions of years ago, tons upon tons of plant and animal debris drifted down through the ocean depths and became trapped in sand or rocks on the bottom. As eons passed, the restless earth added more layers above these sedimentary traps at the sea floor. By process of decay, the debris formed hydrocarbon compounds that included natural gas.

Tremendous pressure was created by the gas, but because of the impermeable layers of rock and sand above, it could not escape to the surface. Oil was formed, trapped for millennia in subterranean reservoirs.

Although we commonly think of these reservoirs as gaping, liquid-filled underground caverns or cavities, they are actually deposits squeezed into the strata of rocks and sand, sometimes covering vast areas of the earth's interior.

Some of these deposits now lie beneath solid rock layers several thousand feet thick. They formed in most areas of the world. Some were very small and isolated; others, under the tremendous pressures, slowly migrated or spread to join others and form huge pools. When we speak of "oil" we really mean petroleum, which is composed mainly of complex combinations of hydrogen and carbon, called hydrocarbons, and some organic compounds containing sulfur, nitrogen, and oxygen in varying amounts.

Most petroleum is found in rocks that were deposited under saltwater conditions, even though some such areas are no longer under water. Huge petroleum deposits have been found some six thousand feet below the surface of dry, mainland Canada, for instance, but at some time in geologic history the area was covered with great coral limestone reefs along the shoreline of some ancient tropical sea. In a few places of the world—the Soviet Union, China, Romania, and eastern Venezuela, as ex-amples—substantial oil deposits lie in rocks of freshwater origin.

A very few of the oil deposits migrated to the surface where early man could observe them as oil seeps, mentioned briefly in the first chapter. Denied the tools and technology of today's advanced age, man could only scoop up the small amount of oil he saw on the ground and adapt it to his needs.

It was in the Middle East that early civilizations first made use of this naturally oozing oil. Ancient inscriptions unearthed in Mesopotamia indicate that prehistoric man found uses for petroleum as early as 4000 B.C. And historians have noted that Alexander the Great, about 331 B.C., was startled to see a giant column of flame spouting from the earth, probably a natural gas fire near an oil seep.

For a long time, man's only other major energy sources were wood and coal, which he burned to keep warm and to cook his food. Although coal was a relatively economical source of energy, it had one major disadvantage—it was dirty. Burned in

37

Small motor vessel maneuvers a loaded coal barge on the Monongahela River, near Morgantown, West Virginia. This barge contains approximately 900 tons of coal which will be transported to a nearby generating station.

furnaces to provide heat and to power machines, its sooty residue blackened all around it, and even endangered human health. Today, coal reserves in the United States are sufficient to fulfill the nation's energy demand for many years, but no way has yet been found to use it without polluting.

To a limited degree, various animal oils—such as whale oil —have been used to fuel lamps, and for cooking. Man also harnessed wind and water power with windmills and water-wheels.

But not until the nineteenth century, millions of years after petroleum began to form in the earth, did man discover its vast potential and begin to mine it in earnest.

It was in the United States that the earth's fossil fuel reservoirs were tapped for the first time on a commercial scale. On August 27, 1859, five years after the invention of the kerosine lamp, oil was discovered by Edwin L. Drake beside aptly named

This photograph, taken near Titusville, Pennsylvania, shows in top hat and frock coat, Edwin L. Drake, the man who conceived the idea of drilling for oil. On August 27, 1859, he proved his theory with the primitive rig pictured in the background.

Barrels by the thousands were used by oilmen in the early days of the petroleum industry for the storage and transportation of oil. Shown above is an 1885 photograph of the array of barrels laid out in front of the first oil well in Findlay, Ohio.

Oil Creek in Titusville, Pennsylvania. Drake had been drilling for the Seneca Oil Company, an early pioneer firm in the oil exploration field. Compared to the several-thousand foot depths to which oilmen drill today, Drake's well was hardly more than an oil seep—oil was struck at only sixty-nine feet below the surface.

Yet it touched off a technological explosion that has not subsided since. Drilling for oil in the United States spread rapidly after 1859, extending westward to California in 1865. The first Texas production well was drilled in 1887, and the first oil refinery began operation in 1860, only a mile from Drake's famous well in Pennsylvania.

For years, dry land wells in the United States and other countries produced all the oil the world needed. But the demand suddenly skyrocketed in the early twentieth century after a single invention: the internal combustion engine.

Powering much of the world's industry, as well as its millions of motor vehicles, ships, trains, and airplanes, this engine uses gasoline or diesel—refined from crude petroleum—as an energy source. Combustion engines vary in function and detail, but all rely on the same basic principles. Liquid fuel is vaporized, usually by a carburetor, and inserted into a cylinder. Highly volatile, it is then ignited by an electric spark. The explosion moves a piston which in turn is coupled to other machinery which transmits the energy to a drive train.

The total oil energy demand of the automobile, particularly the American automobile, is staggering to behold. American cars alone burn some 7 million barrels of petroleum every day. That is almost as much as the Soviet Union's total petroleum demand, substantially more than Japan's.

Until quite recently, American automobiles were larger and heavier proportionately than their foreign counterparts. They therefore burned more gasoline or diesel per mile of travel. An increasing awareness of the world's energy shortage has brought about a demand for smaller, lighter, and more economical cars in the United States. Still, governments have experienced difficulty in enticing commuting motorists to form gas-saving motor pools, and mass transit systems—such as urban bus and train

An oil field in West Texas.

networks—are far less in use in the United States than in many countries.

As the era of the automobile began in the United States, oil production began to blossom. By 1903, California had become

the leading production state, but Oklahoma production sur-
passed California's only five years later. By 1930, when a major
oil field was discovered on the prairies of East Texas, that state
became the undisputed leader, and oil has played a major role

A drilling rig rises out of a cotton field in Oklahoma. Oilmen are careful that their operations do not interfere with other activities in the area.

in the development of the nation's second largest state.

The spiraling demand for oil products after Drake's discovery can be appreciated from a few statistics. In 1918, the year that World War I ended and peacetime use of oil replaced wartime demands, total American oil production was 356 million barrels annually. Only twenty years later, in 1938, it had nearly quadrupled, to 1,214,000,000 barrels.

Today, the United States, the world's largest oil producer, produces more than 3,500,000,000 barrels of oil each year; its daily refining capacity is 14 million barrels.

Looking at these figures, and considering that American oil *consumption* continues to rise at the rate of more than 7 percent each year (more than one-third of the world's total), it is easy to understand why oilmen began looking beyond the conventional dry land sites for new oil reserves.

They found them in the sea.

Technically, the world's first offshore oil wells date back to 1894, only thirty-five years after Edwin Drake began producing oil in Pennsylvania. But those wells were not the kind we are familiar with today. True, they were drilled underwater—in California's oil-rich Santa Barbara Channel—but the drilling equipment itself was placed on wooden wharves on the shore. Drills were extended on a slant from wharf to sea; the oil produced was then taken ashore by pipeline, and refined.

The first true offshore wells were drilled in the Gulf of Mexico, off the coast of Louisiana, in 1936. Only twelve years later, they had extended so far beyond the Gulf shore that workers on the drilling platforms could no longer see land. Gulf oil production boomed two years later with the discovery of the famed Creole Field. Even today, the Gulf is called the "Oil Patch" by oilmen, a reference both to its high oil productivity

and its historic role in ocean oil mining.

Offshore drilling began to proliferate in the years following, as geologists perfected new techniques for finding deposits, and as engineering advances made deeper drilling possible.

While it took the oil industry twenty years to drill effectively from a fifty-foot deep water level to six hundred feet, the working depth *doubled* in the following ten years. By 1967, oilmen were drilling routinely in depths of twelve hundred feet, and there are serious predictions that depths of six thousand feet—more than a mile down—will be possible within the next few years.

The risks of drilling in the sea obviously exceed those on dry land. Added to the normal problems of drilling are swift ocean currents, waves, and storms. Hurricanes with winds of more than one hundred miles an hour occur in the Gulf of Mexico. The North Sea, located between the British Isles and the European mainland, now an intensely developed oil area, is noted for its savage winter storms. Waves as high as one hundred feet have been observed there in recent history.

And the Gulf of Alaska, which oil tankers began transiting in 1977 carrying oil from the port of Valdez after it flowed eight hundred miles south via pipelines from Alaska's North Slope, is equally noted for its fierce weather.

It is a fact of the oilman's life today that much of the earth's area where he must drill is harassed by severe weather. This, of course, increases the possibility of oil spills, a problem already compounded by the simple mathematics of more and more oil being produced and transported.

Opposite: A modern offshore oil platform with service vessel tied alongside.

A supply boat departs from a production platform in the North Sea.

Elaborate safety procedures have been established by the oil industry to prevent accidental well blowouts that could result in spills. The major problem in drilling is pressure. Once a well is drilled through the rock or sand overburden to reach the oil

48

below, there exists an opening through which oil and gas attempt to escape. It is then necessary to somehow block the well to keep the gas-pressured oil from rushing to the surface as the drill is removed from the drill shaft.

The usual procedure is to pump heavy drilling mud down through the drill, which is hollow, into the cavity below it. Drilling mud is ordinary mud combined with a chemical that thickens as it is released. If the correct amount of mud is pumped in, it will balance the pressure of oil and gas and none will escape.

A second well safety feature is a device that oilmen call a *blowout preventer*. It is, simply explained, a plug that can be screwed into the drill hole after the drill has been removed.

The two methods do not automatically prevent blowouts, however. Drillers must be able to calculate closely the amount of pressure in the hole, how much mud to pump in, and many other factors. Preventing a well blowout, in other words, depends as much on human judgment as it does on equipment.

Errors in judgment can be costly. The cause of the Santa Barbara Channel oil spill in January, 1969, was attributed to an apparent weakness in a section of strata through which a worn-out drill bit was being removed—and failure to detect the weakness.

The water beneath the drilling platform was two hundred feet deep, but the oil reservoir lay much deeper—3,500 feet below the channel floor. Following usual procedure, packing mud was pumped into the hole as the drill was being removed. But there was a thin spot in the layer of rock between the reservoir and the channel floor which no one had noticed. When removing the drill opened a hole at that point, oil, under tremendous pressure of gas, escaped. Before the spill could be

49

controlled, more than 4 million gallons of oil spewed into the channel and blackened thirty miles of beaches.

In terms of volume, an even greater spill was that involving a production platform in the North Sea in April, 1977. It began as roustabouts (the oilman's term for oil-well laborers) attempted to install a blowout preventer. Apparently, not enough drilling mud had been pumped into place. The oil shot out of the sea as a huge gusher; the greatest of all human strength could not replace the preventer in time.

The accident spilled more than 8 million gallons of oil into the North Sea before a team of spill cleanup experts, flown from the United States, was able to cap the runaway well many days later.

Considering the tremendous volume of oil produced offshore worldwide since the first Gulf of Mexico wells were drilled in the 1930s, and the inherent risks of their operation, the fact that only a very few have resulted in major spills is a tribute to the skills of the oil industry.

3

GROWTH OF THE TANKER

In 1886, a ship named the *Glückauf* was built and launched in England for a German shipowner. Those watching her slide down the ways noted that she was not at all like most other ships they had seen joining the world's merchant fleet.

Having a 3,020-ton capacity, the *Glückauf* was, by today's standards, modestly built. Three hundred feet long, she had a beam of only thirty-seven feet, and compared to even contemporary vessels of her period, she was somewhat ordinary. What set the *Glückauf* apart from her sister ships was the fact that she was the world's first vessel designed specially to transport oil in bulk. She was the world's first oil tanker.

Her propulsion machinery and boilers were situated aft, not in the center like most other ships, and were separated from the forward cargo tanks by a double bulkhead. This way, the weight of the cargo forward would be balanced by that of the propulsion machinery and superstructure aft.

The *Glückauf* was the first of a succession of specially designed vessels which today have become the largest vessels afloat.

51

Much oil is moved across the United States via pipeline. This is an above-ground section of the Trans-Alaska pipeline near Livengood, Alaska.

They owe their existence to the fact that oil is rarely consumed near the place where it is found; it must be transported.

In the United States, pipelines usually move crude oil from producing wells to refineries. The pipelines are laid both underground from dry land wells to refineries, or on or under the seabed, as from Gulf of Mexico offshore platforms to coastal refineries and storage areas. More than half of the earth's proved oil reserves, outside the Soviet Union and China, are located in the Middle East nations bordering the Arabian-Persian Gulf. Others are in the Western Hemisphere, West Africa, and Southeast Asia, often in remote areas.

Oil refineries, such as this one in the United Kingdom, convert crude oil into useful products.

The oil has no value until it is delivered to refineries and converted into useful products by nations which need it. Japan, a heavy petroleum user, has practically no oil of its own. Europe imports about 70 percent of its oil; the United States, nearly half.

To fill this need, there is no alternative to specially designed ships—tankers, or tank ships—to carry oil over vast stretches of ocean. Every day, more than 38 million barrels of crude oil and petroleum products are loaded aboard tankers somewhere in the world for delivery somewhere else. To better understand how much oil that is, picture a lake one acre in size and five thousand feet deep; that is an approximate equivalent.

By 1900, the world's tanker fleet had grown to about one hundred ships, the largest not much bigger than the *Glückauf*, and the fastest designed for a speed not exceeding nine knots.

World War I demanded a steady flow of petroleum products across the Atlantic to fuel tanks, airplanes, and other mechanized weapons. It was at this point in history that tankers began growing suddenly larger, faster, and more costly—and each with a greater potential for damage if an accident occurred.

During World War II, tankers designated as "T-2s" were common. They averaged about 16,500 DWT. Following the war, ships of 25,000 tons came on the scene, and only a few years later, the 100,000-ton mark was passed. In the 1960s, the age of the *supertanker* arrived with the launching of the first 200,000-ton vessel.

Generally speaking, any tanker over 160,000 tons is considered a VLCC—Very Large Crude Carrier. Considering that the largest tanker in use today, the *Batillus*, is 550,000 tons, tankers have increased their cargo capacity *165 times* since the tiny *Glückauf* began plying the sea lanes less than a century ago.

The tanker Batillus *on its maiden voyage in 1976.*

The largest tankers now afloat are more than three times the size of the U.S. Navy's nuclear aircraft carrier *Enterprise.*

The largest of the supertankers, like the *Batillus,* are referred to as Ultra Large Crude Carriers, or ULCCs.

The larger a tanker is, the more oil it can carry, and the greater the responsibility for its operation at sea and in port. The risk of an accident is multiplied. Moving through the ocean at cruising speed, it takes more than four miles to bring one of the larger tankers to a dead stop, for instance, and turning a VLCC requires careful advance planning. Large tankers are much more difficult to maneuver in crowded harbors because they are more vulnerable to wind.

Most modern tankers are equipped with an array of electronic aids to make navigation safer, and many such aids are required by law. With radar, for instance, tanker masters can "see" other ships—even tiny ones, and even at night—at great distances, and give maneuvering orders to avoid collision.

The economics of oil production and transportation have largely dictated the move to bigger and bigger tankers. Large tankers are generally more efficient than smaller ones. For instance, a 275,000-ton tanker is only twice as long, twice as wide, and twice as deep as a 21,000-ton tanker. Yet it carries thirteen times as much oil. The reason is that the carrying capacity (or volume) of a ship increases at a much faster ratio than the external dimensions.

Larger ships also conserve energy. On a voyage to Europe from the Middle East, for instance, a 275,000-ton tanker can deliver twenty-eight barrels of oil for every barrel of fuel consumed. A 50,000-ton vessel can deliver only about thirteen barrels for every barrel it uses. One reason for the savings is the increased hydrodynamic efficiency of larger hulls. A larger tanker moves through the water with less resistance, in proportion to its size, than a smaller one. And the engines need not be enlarged as much proportionately to the ship's size, so operating costs are reduced.

In one specific way, the trend toward larger supertankers, the VLCCs and the ULCCs, increases the risk of oil spills. Such ships have become so large that many world ports are too small or too shallow to accommodate them. Except for two ports on the West Coast, San Francisco and Los Angeles, no American harbor is deep enough to receive tankers of more than 80,000 tons. But even the West Coast ports cannot accommodate the largest of the tankers.

It is obvious that transferring oil in the open ocean is riskier

*Offloading of oil from a larger tanker to a smaller one. This opera-
tion was conducted about 120 miles offshore.*

than in a protected harbor. It would be economically impossible to widen and deepen most harbors to accommodate the super-tankers. One solution proposed is the development of ports offshore—floating docks and storage terminals anchored to the sea bottom, and protected by floating breakwaters. Specific proposals have been made for two such offshore ports in the Gulf of Mexico.

Supertankers and their operation are controversial subjects. Their opponents contend that the risk of oil spills increases with size both because of the greater amount of cargo carried and the increased difficulty in operating them.

Supertanker designers, builders, and operators, on the other hand, feel that larger tankers reduce oil spill risk simply because there are fewer vessels involved in carrying a given amount of cargo. As a parallel, they suggest what might happen if all buses, streetcars, and other mass transit vehicles suddenly were removed from a city's streets, and their passengers transferred to individual automobiles. Would that not increase the risk of accidents?

Without question, modern tankers are the products of very advanced design and the latest construction techniques available. Many tanker accidents involve old, outdated ships in which navigation equipment does not always function properly.

After the first VLCCs were placed in operation, the American Bureau of Shipping (ABS), an international society which classifies ships, sponsored a comprehensive program to measure the actual stresses imposed on large tankers while at sea. The results of the tests, continually being upgraded, are used in future tanker design.

Like all ships, tankers must comply with national and international regulations covering design, construction, and opera-

An oil slick spreads from the stern section of the 631-foot tanker Irenes Challenge *near Midway Island in the Pacific, January 18, 1977.*

tion. These regulations come from three primary sources. The first includes national agencies, such as the U.S. Coast Guard, that enforce antipollution and safety regulations of all ships, foreign or domestic, operating in American waters.

The second involves international classification societies such as ABS. They inspect and approve ships after completion. Last are international organizations which promote safety standards through agreements between maritime nations. The largest of these organizations is the Intergovernmental Maritime Consultive Organization (IMCO). It was established in 1948 by the United States. It now has more than ninety member nations.

Despite all precautions, tanker accidents continue to occur. In the single four-month period of October, 1976, to January, 1977, eight tanker accidents in the United States alone dumped more than 26 million gallons of petroleum into the sea.

Also, during that period, the tanker *Irenes Challenge* sank off the Pacific island of Midway, dumping 9,600,000 gallons of light crude. Another 8 million gallons of oil was lost when the tanker *Grand Zenith* ran aground and broke up off Cape Sable, Nova Scotia. And in Alaska's Cook Inlet, 1,260,000 gallons of jet aviation fuel were dumped in an accident involving the vessel *Sea Lift Pacific*.

But during that same four-month period, an estimated 192 *billion* gallons of petroleum products were carried and delivered safely by tanker somewhere in the world.

The oil delivered without incident received little publicity. That lost in accidents was major news, for once again it raised an important question. *How damaging is oil once spilled into the marine environment?*

4

OIL CAN DESTROY

Mariners caught by storms at sea developed a simple technique years ago to calm the fury of the waves. They carried a can or bag filled with oil. When a storm threatened their vessel, they pricked holes in the container and allowed the oil to seep slowly into the sea. The oil reduced the power of the waves, and gave the ship temporary protection.

That kind of oil slick undoubtedly saved many human lives. But in more modern times, oil slicks have meant only death or damage to many forms of animal and plant life, a costly mess to clean up, a threat to the marine ecosystem.

Oil spills *do* cause damage. But only in the past decade or so have scientists begun to determine what kind of damage, how much, how long-lasting, and at what cost to the ocean environment.

No two oil spills are alike. One spill may involve only a small amount of oil, yet cause heavy damage. Another may involve a massive amount of pollutants, yet cause little damage. It all depends upon the conditions under which the spill occurs, and they can be as varied as the vagaries of the sea itself.

Nor are all oils alike. Oil comes in thousands of different compounds and weights. Even crude oils, the raw petroleum product as it comes out of wells, differ. Some crudes contain higher percentages of sulphur and other chemicals, so their effects on the marine environment may differ.

Let's take a look at an "average" oil spill to see how oil behaves once spilled into the ocean.

With few exceptions, oil is lighter than water. When a medium-weight crude oil spills into the sea, it rises to the surface. It drifts about, pushed by winds and waves. It spreads out, though not always uniformly. Part of the oil slick, mostly on the outer fringes, thins down to within fractions of an inch.

Almost immediately, some of the oil begins to evaporate. Some hydrocarbons go fairly rapidly, others more slowly, as the slick is affected by sunlight. In rough seas, some of the slick is removed by sea spray. Droplets containing hydrocarbons may be carried as far away as fifty miles. Then they either re-enter the sea or evaporate into the atmosphere.

In spots, what remains of the oil may take on a puddinglike consistency. With continued wave action, these patches dissipate rapidly. In the case of unrefined crude oils or heavier fuel oils such as Bunker C, they form tar lumps or tar balls.

As matter in the sea is gathered by these sticky lumps, some of the lumps sink. Many tiny animals feed on this material. One type is a tiny crustacean, the copepod, that eats the tar and excretes it as a dense feces. Microorganisms also feed on oil internally and degrade it, ultimately as an innocuous CO_2, or water.

Currents also affect the oil slick and its tar balls. Depending upon their velocity, they further dissipate the oil as oxidation

The stranded tanker Argo Merchant *lies helpless off Nantucket Shoals after wreck in December, 1976.*

continues. The lifetime of these lumps may range from a few months to a year. Sometimes they last much longer. What remains of an oil slick after that time will not be easy to detect, even by scientists with special detection equipment.

For instance, not long after the tanker *Argo Merchant* ran aground off Nantucket Shoals on the East Coast in December, 1976, and spilled an estimated 7,600,000 gallons of crude oil into the sea, the spreading slick dissolved into tar balls. There were great fears for the safety of fish populations, shellfish, and humpback whales in the area. Scientists tracked the slick for several days. But later, when it broke up, its remains could no longer be detected.

63

Not all oil spills linger long. A type of oil that might react differently would be what oilmen call Kuwait crude. A light oil, containing less than 2 percent sulphur, this was the type spilled by the tanker *Torrey Canyon* off the coast of Great Britain in 1967. That accident was considered a major spill and did much damage. However, many scientists later contended that it was a lack of knowledge of spill cleanup techniques at the time, not merely the oil itself, that contributed to the damage.

An oil called Jobo, an unusual crude oil from Venezuela, would react on the other end of the scale. It will not float, dissipates very slowly, and is not biodegradeable (digestible by bacteria).

Another factor that varies with oil is its toxicity, or content of poisonous elements. Generally speaking, refined oils or distillates are more toxic than crude oil. Among the oils having the most toxic effect is No. 2 fuel oil, a refined distillate.

Heavier oil, regardless of its degree of toxicity, causes damage through physical smothering.

Oil spilled in shallow coastal waters more likely will be devoured by organisms such as microbes and bacteria than oil spilled in the open sea. The reason is simply that there are many more such organisms along the coast than offshore. Marine scientists have learned that many ocean areas far from land are in essence biological "deserts," almost totally lacking life.

In the open sea, evaporation and photochemical reaction from sunlight have great effects on a spill. And the greater the rate and extent of the spreading of an oil slick, the greater the rate of evaporation. Evaporation alone removes about half of the hydrocarbons in an average crude oil spill on the ocean's surface. As much as 75 percent of lighter fuels—gasoline, as an example—will evaporate under the same conditions.

Even after dozens of studies prompted by major oil spills in the late 1960s and early 1970s, scientists still have much to learn about the fate and effects of oil in the ocean. They still know very little, for instance, about the actual rates of biological degradation of petroleum in the sea under varied conditions of temperature, depth, and location.

But patterns are beginning to emerge from the scientific study to help us better understand spills and how to best prevent them and clean them up in the future. We now know many of the factors that determine whether a spill will cause heavy, long-lasting biological damage, little or no damage, or damage to some intermediate degree.

Two actual spills, which scientists studied in great detail, provide excellent comparative examples.

Perhaps the most famous of all oil spills was the blowout of Platform A in the Santa Barbara Channel of California in January, 1969. It involved crude oil being produced offshore. An estimated ninety-five thousand barrels (4 million gallons) leaked out altogether. Although within sight of the shoreline, the drilling platform was situated in an open channel, through which current flowed, and which was affected by tides.

In March, 1957, twelve years before the Santa Barbara spill, the tanker *Tampico Maru* ran aground off the coast of Mexico's Baja California peninsula and drifted ashore into a small, confined cove. The broken vessel spilled sixty thousand barrels (about 2,770,000 gallons) of toxic diesel fuel, which covered two miles of shoreline.

Exhaustive scientific studies were made following both spills. The scientists involved were at a disadvantage; in neither case had an earlier *baseline* study been made. A baseline is a known starting point for comparative analysis. The normal temperature of the human body, for instance, is known to be 98.6 degrees Fahrenheit. If body temperature exceeds or is lower than this, doctors know that something is wrong. If the normal temperature were unknown, any temperature reading would be meaningless.

In other words, in the case of the two spills, there were no clear pictures of what the biological communities were like *before* the spills occurred. Scientists, however, could estimate with considerable accuracy from knowledge of similar areas. This they coupled with what they saw after each spill.

The most immediate effect of both spills was visual. Pushed by currents and tides, drifting oil reached the nearby shoreline, smearing everything in its path with an unpleasant goo. In the Baja California cove, which was unpopulated and remote from cities or towns, this may not have mattered as much, as far as aesthetic loss was concerned. But the Santa Barbara Channel slick brought about a massive cleanup effort because it reached beaches which are a popular, year-round recreation source.

Many birds—possibly as many as thirty-six hundred—died in the Santa Barbara spill, mainly as they dived through the oil slick, or as they swam across it. Many intertidal organisms were smothered and died.

Yet except for these, according to a study by the University of Southern California, there was no long-term adverse effect of the Santa Barbara oil. Fish and plankton apparently were unaffected. There was no directly attributable damaging effect of oil on large marine mammals, or on bottom-dwelling animals. The channel is a popular sportsfishing region; in the year after the spill the fish catch was about equal to that recorded a year earlier.

66

Such was not the case with the *Tampico Maru*. Investigating the cove three weeks after the tanker accident, a biologist, Dr. Wheeler J. North of the California Institute of Technology, found almost total immediate devastation.

Although seaweeds survived with only minor damage, Dr. North later reported, "The luxurious submarine gardens in the cove and surrounding beaches perished." Only a few marine animals and plants remained in the vicinity of the wreck.

Yet even though no cleanup of the cove was attempted, life slowly returned. Three months after the spill, large swimming animals—fishes, sea lions, lobsters—came back. Tiny organisms such as certain bryozoans, which live only a few weeks or months, began repopulating barren areas. Seaweeds, given a chance to grow when certain animal predators were destroyed by the spill, flourished.

Dr. North, who also dived in the Santa Barbara Channel after the 1969 spill, returned to Baja California every year until 1971. "Things aren't precisely as they were before the wreck," he reported, "but I'd say the biological community has regained its health."

What is perhaps best illustrated by these two examples is that while most biological communities eventually recover after an oil spill, how long that takes varies widely.

As indicated in the first chapter, the loss of marine life following the *Metula* spill in South America was particularly long-lasting. Yet a scientist who studied California's San Francisco Bay after a tanker accident in 1971, said the replacement of such organisms as barnacles, mussels, periwinkles, and limpets was "almost immediate and outstanding."

The time of year that a spill occurs can greatly influence the degree of damage.

Young salmon fry, hatched in upland streams and lakes, migrate to the ocean where they spend most of their lives. If there is an oil spill during the salmon's migrating "run," the loss may be high. Crab larvae, which float near the surface of the water, will probably be killed if they are smeared with oil during this stage of their life cycle.

By the same reasoning, a spill that fouls a popular recreation beach during the summer months will be considered more serious than in winter when vacationing human crowds are gone.

Currents, wave action, and coastal formation all combine to influence the behavior of an oil spill. So does turbidity, the sediments stirred up and suspended between the water surface and the sea floor.

Turbidity can either adversely or beneficially affect a spill. In some cases, suspended particles act as tiny "blotters," soaking up spilled oil particles and carrying them to the bottom. If the spill site is rich in benthic biota (bottom-dwelling plants and animals) this can be quite harmful, for without the sinking caused by turbidity, they would be unaffected.

But if the area lacks bottom dwellers, sinking oil will probably cause little damage; whatever oil sinks will not drift elsewhere to cause harm.

What happens specifically when wind, current, and tide push a spill onto a shoreline? For marine scientists, the answer is critical, since the shoreline is a vital part of the marine ecosystem. The shore is a meeting of ocean and land, and it is here that many organisms spend much of their lives, or pass

Opposite: The remains of an oil spill are clearly visible on this beach in the Chesapeake Bay area.

Scientist testing the effects of oil spilled near the shore.

through from estuaries and bays to the open sea.

Spills in estuaries can cause considerable damage. For instance, they are frequently bounded by marshes on which dense stands of grasses grow. One acre of marsh may produce more than five tons of grass in a year. When these grasses die and decompose, they wash into the estuary at high tide, providing a rich supply of food for many organisms.

Oil spilled in this region can severely upset the marine food cycle, or food chain. The oil enters the marshes, sinks into the sediments. The dilution and evaporation of the toxic components of the spill slow down, and the concentrations can quickly reach a point where marine life in the sediments dies. This includes clams, mussels, oysters, and other organisms that are not only food for marine animals, but for man himself.

Marsh plants also may be coated and killed by oil. Thus, another important source of food for marine life has vanished. Once again, the degree of damage depends upon the type of oil involved. It also depends upon the age of the oil.

In one study, a team of marine life scientists from the Virginia Institute of Marine Science deliberately spilled oil in a controlled section of Virginia's York River to determine what would happen. Five segments of a marsh were physically isolated from the surrounding area and doused with fresh crude oil, and oil that had been artificially weathered.

Weathered oil is that which has been exposed to the elements for some time. In the Virginia study, tiny marine plants, snails, and fish all showed greater declines following man-made spills of weathered oils than with fresh crude.

Scientists also know that the effect of an oil spill is influenced by whether the spill is chronic or acute. *Chronic* means oil that has been spilled, usually in small quantities, repeatedly, and

Many shoreline organisms are affected by oil spills.

usually over a long period of time. Natural oil seeps are perhaps the best example. There is also some oil lost routinely in offshore oil production and in small (less than fifty barrels) spills; according to one estimate, it amounts to about .02 million metric tons worldwide per year. Few routine tanker or fuel barge loading and unloading operations are conducted without at least some very minor spillage.

A study by the Gulf University Research Consortium (GURC), a group of thirteen Gulf Coast universities and research institutions, investigated the effect of such chronic pollution on the marine environment. The area studied was a section of the Gulf of Mexico, heavily drilled for many years. The study concluded that despite enormous oil activity there, the Gulf "is in good ecological health" and remains biologically "highly productive."

72

Acute refers to sudden, massive introduction of oil or other pollutants in a major spill such as happened in the Santa Barbara Channel or with the *Tampico Maru* or *Torrey Canyon*. Generally, the damage is greater than with chronic pollution.

So far, we have seen how oil spills can affect marine birds, fish, plants, and other organisms. But what about human beings? Are spills a threat to human health? What is their impact on the more than half of the American population that now lives near the ocean, in a fifty-mile-wide strip of land we call the coastal zone?

As with studies of marine life, scientists still have only partial answers. But they do know that oil pollution has two impacts on people. One is the decline of aesthetic quality and its effect on human physical comfort; this is caused by oil and tar residue deposited on beaches.

The second and potentially more dangerous impact is the direct effect on human health. Cancer-causing agents, polynuclear aromatic hydrocarbons (PNAs), are known to be present in small amounts in crude oils. However, to keep a sense of proportion, it must be remembered that these same compounds are also found in cigarettes, burning coal, oil and refuse, and from motor vehicle exhausts.

The danger to human health from oil spills comes from eating oil-contaminated seafood. A study sponsored by the National Academy of Sciences has concluded, however, that PNA concentrations in polluted seafood is no higher than those found naturally in lettuce, mushrooms, and vegetable oils. Their concentration is lower than that found in fried, grilled, or smoked fish and meats. Concluded the study: "Although it is clear that much more information relating to possible low-level toxic effects of contaminants in all foods would be of great impor-

73

tance, it does not appear that our present information provides a basis for alarm about the health effect of oil spills."

The statement doesn't mean, of course, that oil spills are not harmful to humans, only that we don't yet have enough scientific information to determine whether or not they are.

What scientists have learned about oil spills is at best only a good beginning. Budgets nationally for such investigations run into the millions of dollars annually, and only recently has science begun to search in earnest for much-needed answers.

Beyond determining what spills are doing today, scientists are also concerned with what future spills may do. That possibility is not always an optimistic one.

As one example, a Coast Guard oceanographer, Lieutenant C. R. Weir, has predicted that an oil spill in the Arctic Ocean could subject the earth to a new Ice Age. Increasingly, oilmen are turning to the frozen Arctic as a source of oil.

"We are quite certain," Lieutenant Weir told a meeting of scientists, "that when oil is absorbed by the ocean's ice cover, the ice will be destroyed within two years." Oil-darkened ice, having lost the ability to reflect sunlight, would absorb heat and melt. At some critical point, a chain reaction would begin. Polar ice is a major determining factor in the world's weather.

So-called "little ice ages" of the fourteenth and seventeenth centuries and other unusual occurrences such as the dust bowls in the United States in the 1930s may have been related to changes in the Arctic ice pack, Lieutenant Weir believes. His warning was based on experiments performed at the Navy's Arctic Research Laboratory at Barrow, Alaska.

If an Arctic oil spill did what Lieutenant Weir thinks it might, the long-term effect on man's health and welfare could

74

far exceed that which confronts him today from present oil spills.

Clearly, new ways must be found not only to clean up spills once they have started, but as importantly, new methods must be sought to stop them before they occur.

5

STOPPING OIL SPILLS

On May 26, 1967, two months after the *Torrey Canyon* ran aground on a granite reef on the southwest coast of England, President Richard M. Nixon of the United States issued an historic statement.

Referring to the tanker and her massive oil spill, he said he considered it imperative ". . . that we take prompt action to prevent similar catastrophes and to insure that the nation is fully equipped to minimize the threat of such accidents to health, safety, and our natural resources."

The president's statement, issued in Washington, D.C., was the first major public recognition that oil spills had become a serious international problem, and that something had to be done about them.

Concurrent with his remarks, the president directed the secretaries of the Interior and Transportation to determine how best the nation's resources could be mobilized against the pollution of water by spills of oils and other hazardous substances.

Within only a few weeks, the war against oil spills was declared.

76

Congress passed sweeping new laws dealing with oil spill prevention, and authorized penalties for violators of antipollution laws. The Coast Guard received authority to enforce new regulations concerning tanker safety. Private industry joined in, too, organizing interindustry, cooperative, spill cleanup brigades, forming oil spill training schools, and seeking better devices to protect oil production equipment against spill hazards.

In universities and research centers, scientists began pursuing a new discipline: the fate and effects of oil in the marine environment. And to coordinate the effort, a new federal organization was born, the Environmental Protection Agency (EPA).

Almost as the battle against oil spills began, there was sudden and alarming evidence that it had come none too soon. On January 28, 1969, an oil production platform in California's Santa Barbara Channel suddenly released the first of 4 million gallons of crude oil. Although later scientific investigation disclosed that the spill did not cause the permanent damage that was at first feared, the spill galvanized public action, and proved that oil spills were no longer a minor concern.

The total cost of oil spill prevention, cleanup, and control cannot be stated exactly. But it runs into millions of dollars each year, and involves the participation of thousands of people.

The causes of the spills they are concerned with are many—equipment failure, human error, collision, natural disasters. Increasingly, it has become the philosophy of the federal government that, whatever the cause, most oil spills can be prevented. A major emphasis, therefore, is placed on stopping spills before they occur, monitoring all facilities that handle oil, and, through various surveillance methods, detecting and stopping small spills before they can become large ones.

The EPA and the Coast Guard divide the responsibility for spill prevention. The EPA is responsible for all facilities, both on shore and offshore, that are not related to transportation. Included are facilities that drill, produce, gather, store, process, refine, transfer, and distribute or consume oil or other hazardous substances. The Coast Guard is responsible for transportation-related facilities, including vessels, railroads, tank trucks, and pipelines.

Combined, that is a huge responsibility. In the United States there are about thirty thousand oil storage terminals, tank farms, and bulk oil plants alone. There are also about 285 oil refineries and several thousand production facilities. That number changes almost daily as old fields are reopened, stripped and closed, or abandoned. In addition, EPA must police many bulk oil consumers such as houses, office buildings, schools, hospitals, farms, and government facilities, each a potential contributor to the oil spill problem.

The widespread concern over oil spills has generated a wide array of devices which monitor the flow of oil wherever it occurs, whether on offshore platforms, in refineries, or in storage plants. Usually electronic in design, they sound an alarm if something goes wrong.

It is useful, too, to know what *might* happen if oil or another hazardous substance should be suddenly dumped into the sea. The EPA in the early 1970s began operating a facility designed to do just this. It is a computerized system called the Oil and Hazardous Materials Technical Assistance Data System, abbreviated OHM-TADS. Its main function is to tell what kind of substance is involved in the spill, and thus provide information on how best to clean it up.

Here's how OHM-TADS works. Let's say the operator of a

In 1976, construction neared completion on four, half-million barrel crude oil storage tanks in the West Tank Farm at the Valdez Terminal of the Trans-Alaska pipeline.

chemical facility in Ohio detects a leak in his plant. An unknown liquid substance is leaking onto the ground. He contacts the OHM-TADS office by telephone and describes the substance as accurately as he can: its color, consistency, smell, how fast it is flowing.

OHM-TADS' computer previously has stored up information on more than nine hundred different chemical compounds,

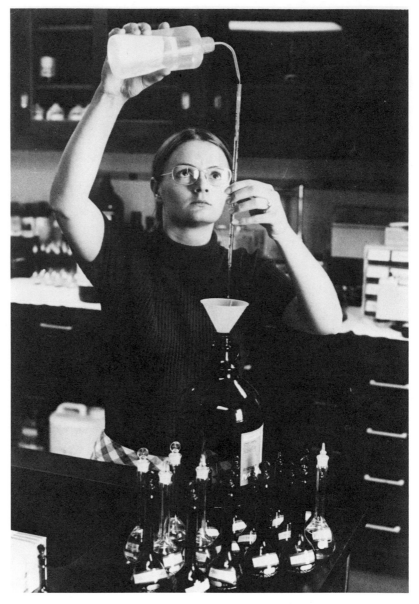

Oil samples are prepared for analysis in the Coast Guard Research & Development Center laboratory in Groton, Connecticut.

including many oils. Usually in fifteen minutes, the computer can tell the chemical plant operator what kind of compound is involved. And, as importantly, it can suggest, from experience, what methods will best clean it up.

In Groton, Connecticut, the Coast Guard runs a similar facility. As we have seen, oils are not alike. Even crude oils vary. Although the human eye usually cannot tell the difference, highly sensitive chemical analysis can.

In Groton, the Coast Guard has accumulated what it calls an "oil fingerprint" file. Use of the word "fingerprint" suggests that, like human fingerprints, oil contains individual characteristics that identify it as distinctively its own. Chemical data on various oil types are stored in a computerized data bank. Samples of oil from a spill can be quickly matched up with other samples on file. The information is useful not only in locating oil spill violators, but in determining the best method for cleaning up a spill.

Monitoring need not always require such modern devices, however. Sometimes, nature provides her own warning of an impending oil spill. Professor D. G. Shaw of the University of Alaska learned from experiments, for instance, that a species of clam tends to burrow deeper into the seabed than usual when abnormal amounts of oil are present. Monitor the behavior of the clam, *Macoma balthica,* Professor Shaw suggested, and scientists have a highly useful "alarm clock" at their disposal.

Even with stronger laws, spills doubtless will continue to occur, but early detection may help clean them up before major damage can result. Surveillance is especially valuable in detecting large spills, such as those from tanker accidents, offshore well blowouts, storage lagoon facilities, catastrophic storms, and pipeline failures.

81

The latter are a frequent spill cause. Each year in the United States, pipeline breaks and leaks cause about five hundred spills, discharging more than 1 million gallons of oil. Since many pipelines are buried underground or below the seabed, a leak may go undetected for years, so it is important to know as early as possible when there is a spill-causing break or leak.

Surveillance systems are becoming increasingly more accurate and sophisticated. For instance, a Massachusetts firm has designed a monitor, operating on an infrared principle, that can detect spills or leaks as small as one part per million, without sampling, testing, or water contact. Whether installed in a refinery or aboard a tanker, the device triggers an alarm if oil is detected. (One part per million means one part of oil per million parts of water.)

The Coast Guard conducts an advanced surveillance system which uses electronic devices carried aboard airplanes patrolling the coastline. The devices include "side-looking radar," television scanners, and extremely sensitive cameras to monitor oil tanker traffic and other potential sources of spills.

The system is abbreviated AOSS, for Airborne Oil Surveillance Systems. In 1975, AOSS first proved its value by detecting a tanker illegally discharging oil off the California coast. The equipment made a permanent record of the violation. Confronted later with the evidence in court, the shipping company involved paid a $4,000 fine.

Predicting what oil spills will do before they even happen is yet another advance of modern science. Fast response is important in cleaning up an oil spill, and there are immediate questions to consider. Which way will a slick drift? Will it sink or float? Will it break up into smaller slicks? What kind of equipment should be rushed to the scene?

82

By using computers, *models* are designed to furnish needed answers. A model is any kind of smaller, simulated representation of the real object. In the case of oil spills, a computer model is a re-creation, on paper, of how the spill probably will behave. That is determined by "programming" the computer with many bits of information: the type of oil spilled, the physical environment in which it is spilled, wind, tides, currents.

Such computer models have proved to be of great value. Focusing on busy New York Harbor, for instance, two scientists with the Coast Guard's Groton, Connecticut, research facility have developed a model that helped control a spill which could have become a major, heavily damaging one.

The need for the model was obvious. Despite the fact that between fifty and one hundred spills occur in the harbor every year, information on how they could best be controlled was meager. Drawing on records of the Army Corps of Engineers and other sources, the Coast Guard programmed information on New York Harbor weather, tides, currents, and other phenomena.

On May 8, 1976, a barge carrying ten thousand barrels of No. 6 fuel oil struck an underwater object near Ellis Island, dumping three thousand gallons within minutes. The computer model was consulted, and proved useful in predicting the flow of the slick. It saved valuable time in deciding how much and what kind of equipment to dispatch to the scene. Based on that experience, the Coast Guard later decided to install similar computer models in San Francisco Bay, Long Island Sound, and Alaska's Cook Inlet.

Training programs are helpful in preparing for spills. As an example, Texas A&M University has operated an oil spill school since 1975. It has trained more than one thousand students

Students at the Texas A & M University's oil spill training school rig a containment boom to a boat for towing.

Here students launch a weir-type skimmer in order to remove simulated oil.

from more than fourteen countries. School sessions last five days, and include both classroom study and actual, on-the-scene, spill cleanup instruction.

Students, most of them from the oil industry, learn how to clean up spills with latest techniques and methods. The training is realistic, except that the "oil" spill they are taught to mop up in Texas' Galveston Bay consists not of the real thing, but of harmless cottonseed hulls.

Cottonseed hull, intentionally spilled into Galveston Bay, is contained by students at the oil spill training school.

A related national preparedness program involves more than one hundred cooperative antispill contingency agencies. Manned by personnel "loaned" by oil companies on an assigned, 24-hour-per-day alert basis, they now have available, collectively, more than $14 million worth of cleanup equipment.

A typical cooperative is the Corpus Christi Area Oil Spill Control Association, founded in 1970 as a nonprofit Texas corporation. The association, financed jointly by private industry and the federal government, provides manpower and equipment for cleaning up spills that occur in the crescent-shaped section of the lower Texas coastline known as the Coastal Bend.

The Corpus Christi area hums with oil activity. The possibility of spills there is great. The port of Corpus Christi, one of the nation's largest, services six major oil refineries, several oil transfer and pipeline terminals, and many chemical and other industrial plants.

Many petroleum storage and shipping facilities dot the fifty-mile shoreline. These are fed via various marine transports and pipelines traversing the waters. Altogether, they carry more than 300 million barrels of oil and other petroleum products each year. The same waters harbor nearly six hundred producing gas and oil wells.

So far, the association has responded to more than two hundred spills. Records show that, on an average, it costs about $1.24 for each gallon of oil cleaned up. That cost may sound high (it is about twice the cost of a gallon of gasoline in a service station), but the reason is that most spills cleaned up have been small ones. There are certain fixed costs in fighting oil spills, and they remain the same regardless of the size of a spill.

When it comes to saving the environment from oil damage,

however, costs are perhaps secondary in importance. In July, 1974, for instance, a crude oil barge went aground in an intra-coastal canal opposite the Aransas National Wildlife Refuge. The refuge is in a remote, isolated area about ninety-five miles from Corpus Christi. It is one of the nation's most environmentally sensitive areas, as it is the winter home of the endangered whooping crane.

About twenty-five barrels of oil spilled from the barge, all of which flowed into the marshy area where the cranes were wintering. Twenty-five barrels may seem like a trivial amount compared to spillage from accidents like Santa Barbara and the *Torrey Canyon*. But, uncontrolled, it could have seriously affected, perhaps even wiped out, the remainder of an entire species of birds.

Because of the remoteness of the spill, and the necessity that every possible drop be removed, the cleanup bill ran to $30,891, or nearly $30 per gallon.

Experience has produced many techniques and special equipment for cleaning up oil spills. One of the oldest methods is to set fire to an oil slick. This, of course, cannot be done if the slick is in a confined harbor where damage could result from the fire. But in the open sea, it is perhaps the simplest way to get rid of oil.

When the *Torrey Canyon* ran aground in 1967, one of the first cleanup attempts involved bombing the wreck from English Royal Air Force airplanes. It was hoped that the bombs would ignite the spreading oil. But oil in the sea will catch fire only if it lays thickly, and the *Torrey Canyon* attempt failed.

Because newer methods have been developed, fire is rarely used any longer for cleaning up oil slicks. Cleanup now consists mainly of one of three techniques or a combination of them.

The first two involve picking up spilled oil, either by skimming it from the surface, or by applying absorbent materials which are in turn picked up. The third method is dispersing the oil with chemicals. Dispersed oil usually sinks to the bottom.

The decision of which method to use depends on many factors. Because of winds, tides, and currents, open sea spills are probably the most difficult to clean up. In fact, it is considered impossible to pick up open sea oil if wave heights approach two feet, or the velocity of the wind exceeds two knots. Newer equipment is constantly being designed which may soon overcome these limitations, however.

In picking up spilled oil directly, skimmers or booms are

Opposite: A floating weir-type oil skimmer developed primarily to remove oil and other floating pollutants from surface of protected waters. Weir has no moving parts; it is operated by remote control from shore.

Below: A skimmer used for cleaning up oil spills in harbors. Oil and water are separated by a system of baffles within barge-like vessel after being scooped up by flexible booms.

A 58-foot oil spill recovery vessel called the Spill Spoiler II. *It is of catamaran type; oil and water to be separated are drawn up through open bow. This vessel is operated by Clean Bay, Inc., a San Francisco Bay oil spill cooperative financed by several oil companies.*

used. In skimming, specially designed pickup systems separate oil and water. This technique can be quite successful if the spill is small and well confined, and if the surface of the water is relatively calm. Vacuum skimmers have been used successfully; they work best if the oil layer is relatively thick, and are best suited for picking up oil around piers and ships.

Moving-belt skimmers have also been developed, and used with some success. One type uses a porous belt that allows water to pass through the belt while retaining the oil for collection aboard a boat. Another uses an inverted inclined plane mounted on a catamaran hull. When floating oil encounters a moving solid barrier, it is forced down the slope of the plane and under an open section of the catamaran. Because its specific gravity is lower than that of water, the oil then rises into a collection chamber. From here the oil and perhaps a little water are pumped into storage tanks aboard the vessel.

A self-contained oil skimmer used for spills in large bays, harbors, sounds. Oil and debris are scooped up through open bow. Oil and water are separated inside on a moving belt.

A typical oil containment boom. In use, the boom is towed into place surrounding an oil spill, "corraling" the oil. Debris is then picked up by other equipment.

Floating booms are the second method used in direct oil pickup. They have been designed in many styles. Some are made of solid materials and others are easily stored, inflatable designs. In use, they are first dragged from a vessel around an oil slick, then tightened to "corral" the oil into a smaller area so that it can be picked up.

Oil-absorbent products generally fall into three major classes:

Men of the Coast Guard's Atlantic Strike Force team scoop up samples of an absorbent used to contain an oil spill caused by tropical storm Agnes on the Schuylkill River, Pennsylvania, in 1972. This powdery chemical swells upon contact with water and sops up oil like a sponge.

mineral products, vegetable products, and synthetic products. All are designed to soak up the spilled oil and then be pumped into storage tanks.

Mineral products used include perlite, talc, vermiculite, volcanic ash, and fly ash. The most commonly used vegetable product is straw; more than ten thousand tons of it were used on the 1969 Santa Barbara Channel spill. Synthetic products have included polyurethane, polystyrene, polyester, polyester plastic shavings, urea-formaldehyde resin, resin-type foams, and other plastics.

The disadvantage of absorbents is that as they are applied to a slick, they generate a mass of material far exceeding in bulk the amount of oil they soak up. This requires a greater storage capacity, more equipment, and more manpower than simply scooping up the oil with skimmers or booms.

To overcome this, large vessels now are being designed specifically for cleaning up oil spills. Large storage capacities are a basic requirement of their design.

The final cleanup method is dispersing of oil. Dispersing and chemical dispersing agents are controversial topics. Many scientists maintain that most of the damage following the *Torrey Canyon* spill was caused by the misuse of chemical dispersants. They were applied massively and undiluted. The types were toxic; carrying oil to the bottom, they destroyed many bottom-dwelling organisms.

However, in the years since that spill, chemical dispersants have been developed that are less toxic and more effective. Other scientists say that chemicals pose only a minimum threat to the marine environment if used properly, and may actually prevent significant biological damage.

Except for birds, there is little that can be done once a spill

94

starts, to save plants and animals affected by it. Fish, bottom-dwellers, crustaceans, seaweed, tidepool creatures—only time will replace those that oil's assault has wiped out.

Birds are another matter, and much effort has been expended in saving them. Estimates of damage caused by an oil spill almost invariably begin with the number of birds lost. But the estimates usually are based only on the number of birds found on the shore. Actually, tens of thousands of birds may perish and sink in the open water, after contact with floating oil.

Oiled aquatic birds cannot fly. They lose their insulation from the cold. They cannot float. They become sick; often, they are blinded. As food seekers, waterfowl near a spill may be attracted to dead or dying fish or shellfish in the water, or on shores and beaches, and become affected themselves.

Rescue of oil-soaked birds is generally done at low tide, using nets to avoid harming the birds. They are put in boxes and taken to cleaning stations where detergents are used to remove oil from their feathers. Not all oiled birds can be saved, how-ever; estimates of successful cleaning range only from about 10 to 20 percent.

Sometimes, birds are saved by frightening them away from spills. Alarms, noisemakers, flashing lights, pennants, and many other devices have been used.

Although the techniques for cleaning up oil spills have ad-vanced rapidly since the Santa Barbara and *Torrey Canyon* accidents, even the greatest efforts of science and industry may never completely solve the worsening problem they cause. Ulti-mately, the solution may be one for which dwindling fossil fuel supplies of the earth leave no alternative.

Only in finding newer, nonpolluting sources of energy will oil spills become a fact in history.

6

ENERGY OF TOMORROW

In July, 1968, oil was discovered on Alaska's North Slope. It was one of the biggest "strikes" in the history of oil production; geologists estimated that 9.6 billion barrels of oil eventually could be recovered by drilling in this region which adjoins the Arctic Ocean.

But there were numerous and monumental problems facing prospective miners of Alaskan oil. The major one was transportation. For only a few weeks of the year is the Arctic Ocean free of ice. If tankers were to be used to ship the oil out to world markets, oilmen wondered, could they safely operate in one of the most hazardous of seas?

To find out, eight oil companies involved in the North Slope partnership decided to send a tanker, in summer, through Canada's Northwest Passage to the oil fields at Prudhoe Bay. The Northwest Passage is a series of forbidding bays and inlets stretching generally east-west across the top of Canada, not many miles from the North Pole.

The tanker chosen was the *Manhattan*, a 112,000-ton vessel, which at the time was the largest ship afloat under the American flag. Because she had to plow through floating ice fields on her voyage, the *Manhattan* was fitted with a special ice-crushing bow. This, along with other hull modifications and the cost of the experimental voyage itself, ran up a total bill of more than $40 million.

It took the *Manhattan* nearly a month in 1969 to make the 11,000-mile round trip voyage. There were many perils: fog, winds, crashing waves, icebergs. In Baffin Bay alone, even in midsummer, there are an average of four hundred icebergs.

The *Manhattan* succeeded in reaching Prudhoe Bay on the Arctic Ocean, site of the great oil discovery of the year before. As proof that other, specially modified tankers might follow,

The converted oil tanker Manhattan *which successfully traveled the Northwest Passage of Canada from New York to Alaska's North Slope in 1969.*

the vessel returned to New York with a single, token barrel of North Slope oil aboard.

On that return passage, however, ice tore a small hole in the *Manhattan*'s hull. There was no major damage and no lives were threatened, but later, partly for economical reasons and upon the urging of the Canadian government, the idea of sending future tankers through the Northwest Passage was abandoned.

Still the problem remained: how to ship those millions of barrels of oil from Prudhoe Bay. After the *Manhattan* experiment, it was decided that the best way was by pipeline across the width of Alaska, to the port of Valdez, and then by tanker to West Coast ports.

It took nearly six years before construction of the 800-mile Trans-Alaska Pipeline could begin. Not until 1977 was oil finally delivered to the southern Alaska port of Valdez, where storage facilities had been built to transship the oil to the lower United States.

The major reason for the long delay was the fear of many that the pipeline would disrupt Alaska's fragile ecosystem and cause environmental damage. The possibility of oil spills was a major concern. What happened during that period of delay underscores the lengths to which the oil industry must go these days to safeguard against oil spills and other environmental damage.

Environmental impact studies conducted along the pipeline route, costing many millions of dollars, were an outgrowth of a new national policy at that time. The policy is that any construction project must be proved environmentally harmless, or at least that its benefits and damage must be reasonably in balance, before construction can begin.

98

An aerial view of the 1000-acre Valdez terminal of the Trans-Alaska pipeline.

The Trans-Alaska Pipeline was the largest privately funded construction project in world history. Its total cost exceeded $7.7 billion. More than twenty-one thousand workers were involved in building the pipeline itself, its related pump stations, and the storage-shipping facilities at Valdez.

At peak capacity, the pipeline can carry 2 million barrels

of oil a day. It flows at about four miles per hour, taking about a week to reach Valdez from the North Slope.

The preconstruction environmental studies were numerous. Small amounts of oil were deliberately spilled on sections of tundra to see if damage would result. Tundra is the vast, usually level expanse of Arctic plains. Its minute plant life is very

Below: Caribou graze in view of operating oil rigs on Alaska's North Slope near Prudhoe Bay.

A moose, right center, passes beneath a section of above-ground pipe for the Trans-Alaska pipeline. There are about 800 natural and man-made animal crossings along the pipeline's right-of-way.

fragile, and once destroyed, it takes up to forty years to regenerate.

There was concern, too, that caribou and other Arctic animals would not cross a man-made pipeline, and their migratory path would thus be interrupted. Test sections of pipeline were built, and the animals were seen to cross it without apparent fear.

In addition, a number of scientific "baseline" studies were made so that if an oil spill did occur, scientists would have detailed knowledge of what the biological community had been like before the spill, and damage could be more accurately measured.

Another major concern was the port of Valdez. Although the

harbor is free of ice year-round, its entrance is narrow and there are many other hazards to navigation there. En route between Alaska and American West Coast ports, tankers must cross the Gulf of Alaska where savage storms are not rare. The possibility of accidents that might cause oil spills is great.

To guard against them, the Coast Guard established especially strict safety equipment standards for Alaskan oil tankers. Several test runs were made across the Gulf of Alaska and in practicing loading and unloading of oil at Valdez.

Operating at peak capacity, the port of Valdez has become one of the world's busiest harbors. Its 1,000-acre oil storage area can accommodate up to 510,000 barrels of oil in each of the thirty-two storage tanks that will eventually be built there. A multimillion dollar recovery equipment system was designed to

Oceanographers board their floating laboratory Acona *to begin another series of environmental studies in Port Valdez, Alaska. Studies formed part of broader baseline study of the port.*

A containment boom encircles a 900-foot long tanker docked at Berth 4 during an oil spill equipment drill at the Valdez terminal. The boom would prevent spread of oil in the event of a spill.

protect the tanks from loss of hydrocarbons into the air.

Another feature designed to protect the environment at the terminal is a water ballast treatment plant. Tankers traveling empty often fill oil tanks with seawater ballast for stability and must discharge the water before loading oil. The Valdez plant treats all contaminated ballast water from incoming tankers by a system which settles, skims, chemically treats, and then "floats" the tainted seawater.

The elaborate and costly antipollution facilities of the Alaska pipeline demonstrate man's increasing concern over the possibility of oil spills. The flow of Alaskan oil doubtless will help abate world energy demands for many years, as will oil from other oil-producing areas. But the supply of fossil fuels is not infinite. It took nature millions of years to generate the petroleum reserves now in the earth, and man is using them up at an alarming rate.

How soon will the world's oil run out? In May, 1977, an estimate released by the Massachusetts Institute of Technology placed the end of oil in the present century, if demand does not diminish. The estimate was based on a two-year study by a group of thirty-four leading scientists, economists, and business executives from fifteen nations.

There are two ways in which that possibility may be at least delayed, the study group said. One is by strict conservation of energy now being used, and full development of known oil reserves.

The second is to seek full development of alternative sources of energy to fill the gap left by dwindling petroleum supplies.

Some of the sources are already tapped on a commercial scale. Some are still in the experimental stage. But all seem to have potential. Some examples:

Coal

Coal is an exception to the statement that alternative sources of energy have been tapped only to a limited degree. Coal was once a major source of energy, and even though it is considered a "dirty" fuel, its use is still widespread.

Coal reserves in the United States are abundant. In fact, they account for 90 percent of all known domestic fossil fuel sources. By 1990, American coal production is expected to reach 1.5 billion tons annually, almost double the present production level.

The largest users of coal are electric utilities, accounting for about three-fourths of present coal demand. A considerable

This is Consolidation Coal Company's Robinson Run mine, near Shinnston, West Virginia, where a revolutionary new method of

moving coal directly from the working face underground through a pipeline to the preparation plant on the surface was tested.

Loading machine depositing coal into a shuttle car which will carry the coal to a belt conveyor or to steel mine cars for transportation to the outside of the mine.

amount of American coal is exported.

The U.S. Bureau of Mines estimates that United States coal reserves, measured down to more than a mile in the earth, total about 3.2 *trillion* tons. Considering that only about 800 billion tons of that can be produced with present technology, that's still a lot of energy. At the present production level, it would last one thousand years.

However, new technology is needed to clean up coal, or to convert it in some way to clean-burning gas or synthetics. Coal gasification is still in the experimental stage. The development and commercialization of technology for producing gas and liquids from coal is limited by many technical and environmental factors.

By 1990, however, about 82 million tons of coal per year, or about 5 percent of United States production, is expected to go toward producing synthetic oil or gas.

Oil Shale

Oil locked up in shale rock is a massive natural resource. The Interior Department estimates "easily recoverable" shale oil reserves in the United States at 80 billion barrels. Shale oil recoverable with intensive new technology could reach as high as 600 billion barrels.

But no shale oil has yet been produced commercially in the United States, and the federal government has embarked on a trial program of leasing government land for shale oil development. One method of converting shale to oil is by retorting under tremendous heat. In effect, the "locked-in" oil is melted down to liquid form. Plants to accomplish this would probably cost several hundred million dollars each.

Geothermal

One of the most nonpolluting additional energy sources is geothermal energy. Deep beneath the surface of the earth is a mass of molten rock called *magma*. In its tremendous heat is energy; man has sought for years to tap this power for his own use.

Unfortunately, most of the magma lies too deep for its energy to be useful. In a few areas of the earth's crust, particularly around the rim of the Pacific Basin which geologists call the "Rim of Fire," it does occur closer to the surface. In these locations, magma heats the layers of rock above it. If under-

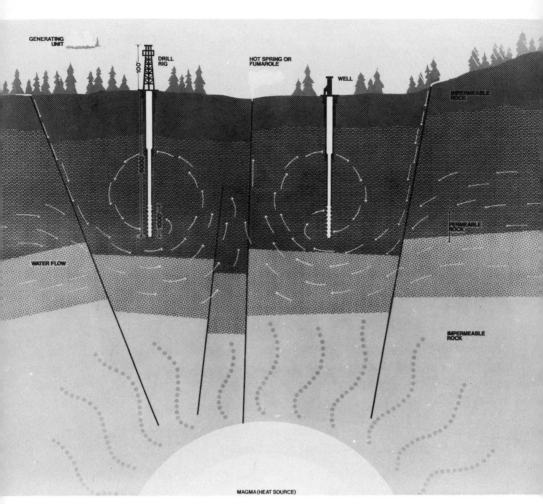

This artist's sketch shows how a geothermal field is developed. Magma, the molten rock found deep in the earth, is the heat source radiating heat energy (wavy dotted lines) through the rock above it. Water flows into the reservoir rock from underground sources and surface runoff. The cool fluids are heated as they come in contact with the hot rock and rise to circulate within the reservoir. A drilling rig penetrates through the impermeable caprock to the top of the reservoir. After drilling is completed, the geothermal energy is piped from the well to an electrical generating unit.

110

A Union Oil Company drilling rig encounters geothermal steam while drilling in The Geysers field in northern California. Conventional oil drilling rigs, specially adapted for geothermal work, are used in tapping the steam deposits which lie sometimes as much as two miles below the surface.

ground water is present it will be heated and rise to the surface, causing such phenomena as hot springs, geysers, and fumaroles (wisps of steam flowing from cracks in the ground). These occurrences can be signposts to earth scientists indicating an area that could produce thermal energy.

Geothermal steam, then, is a sort of natural boiler. Its energy can be harnessed by drilling wells, much as drilling is done for oil or gas, and bringing the fluids or steam to the surface.

More than fifty countries, including the United States, are now active in the development of geothermal steam. Most of the projects are still in the experimental stage, however, although the potential of this added form of energy is considered great.

Experts in government and the geothermal industry believe that 20 million kilowatts of geothermally powered, electrical generating capacity is possible in the next twenty years or so. To put this in perspective, it would require about 700,000 barrels of oil per day to generate the same amount of electricity. That is nearly the entire daily production of the state of California.

Solar Energy

The sun generates more energy each second than man has harnessed from all forms during his entire time on earth. Little wonder, then, that solar energy is one of the brightest hopes of scientists for easing the world's energy crisis.

Solar energy is nonpolluting. Its supply is infinite. Its availability is not subject to international politics. And it can be directed to many specific uses.

Commercially well established in other countries, solar energy to heat water was developed briefly in Florida after World War II when electricity was costly and natural gas was unavailable. Through various methods of capturing the sun's rays, it has been used to directly heat or cool many American homes. It can be harnessed to generate electricity; by using solar "collectors," the energy can be stored up to run generators and other machines.

Until recently, the cost of solar energy, as compared to fossil fuels, was too high for use on a commercial scale. But soaring prices of fossil fuels—oil and gas—have now placed solar energy within financial reach as a major alternative source of power.

Nuclear Power

When American scientists succeeded in splitting the atom in 1945, they at last tapped one of the solar system's almost unlimited sources of energy. But nuclear power as presently produced depends upon the availability of uranium oxide to fuel nuclear reactors. The Atomic Energy Commission estimates that United States reserves of this mineral are about 700,000 tons that can be mined without exorbitant additional costs.

Fuel would not be a problem with what scientists call "fast-breeder" nuclear reactors, however. Unlike nuclear power produced with present technology, they actually produce more fuel than they consume, thus assuring an everlasting supply.

There are many disadvantages of nuclear energy, however, no matter how it is produced. Safety of the plants is one concern. How to best dispose of radioactive wastes produced is another; some of these wastes remain deadly for 500,000 years.

At any rate, commercially produced nuclear energy is already a fact in the United States, though it may be many years, at a staggering cost, before it can be produced on a scale large enough to offset substantially the present demand on fossil fuels.

Windmills, used for centuries as a source of energy, are a possible help in meeting today's energy demand.

In addition to these five sources, there are others which scientists are exploring. To a limited extent, man has harnessed the wind to generate electricity and for other purposes. Captured by wind generators, or windmills, the wind possibly could fill as much as 15 percent of the country's energy demands in a few years.

Hydroelectric power—the harnessing of the energy of moving rivers—is another. Natural gas, which is produced along with oil, is a present major source of power. And in the restless oceans is enough energy to supply *all* of man's power demands, if a way could be found to utilize it effectively at reasonable cost.

The degree to which each of these added energy sources may be utilized depends on many factors. One is an improvement upon current technology. Another is the huge cost involved. And, through scientific research, must be determined priorities of which source to develop first, and to what extent.

Meanwhile, as man continues to rely on earth's dwindling resource of fossil fuels, the battle against oil spills continues. It is increasingly a bigger battle, one to which scientists, engineers, industrialists, and government leaders are devoting considerable time and energy.

It is also a very costly battle, as evidenced by a single spill that occurred near Sein Island off the coast of France.

For reasons never determined by a naval court of inquiry, the East German tanker *Bohlen* ran aground and sank near the island on October 14, 1976. Almost ten thousand tons of Venezuelan crude oil spilled out.

In a unique environmental rescue operation, the French government pumped hot water into the wreckage, three hundred feet beneath the sea, hoping to force the spilling oil to

Oil spills harm not only the environment. In this tanker accident in Los Angeles Harbor, eight persons died.

the surface. There, much of it was burned off.

What local citizens feared most was damage to Sein Island's lobster population, whose succulent seafood had made the place famous as a vacation resort. Many lobsters were blackened by oil. Lobster traps were coated with a sticky, tarlike substance.

The cleanup involved people from all walks of life. Soldiers were dispatched to the scene. Unemployed residents joined in to mop up oil from blackened beaches. The French Navy spread detergents around the island.

In one phase of the cleanup, divers and soldiers were sent to the wreckage of the *Bohlen* in an attempt to patch a hole in her hull through which oil was leaking. The sea was heavy, the winds strong.

Two of the divers and one soldier were trapped in the hole. Before they could be rescued, all died.

The cleanup was successful. A year later, some of Sein Island's beaches still showed signs of oil pollution, but the sea's natural cleansing action scoured most of the fishing grounds and coastline. Today, Sein Island's lobsters, too, are flourishing once again.

The cleanup took six months and the price was staggering. Directly, $30 million was spent. Indirectly, many Sein Island resort facilities lost expected profits when vacationing customers, aware of the oily mess, went elsewhere that season. But the real cost cannot be measured in terms of dollars, and in a sense, it suggests the extent to which oil spills have become a problem in today's world.

Glossary

ASTERN—Behind a ship. At or toward the rear.

BEAM—A ship's width at its widest part.

BRYOZOAN—A group of minute water animals that usually form fixed, mosslike colonies, reproducing by budding.

BULKHEAD—An upright partition separating sections of a ship.

BUNKER C—A heavy crude oil for use in marine vessels.

CRUDE OIL—Unrefined oil.

DEADWEIGHT TONNAGE—A ship's lading, including the total weight of cargo, fuel, stores, crew, and passengers.

ESTUARY—An inlet or arm of the sea.

FOSSIL FUEL—A fuel derived from any rock or mineral dug out of the earth.

HULL—The frame or body of a ship.

HYDROCARBON—Any compound containing only hydrogen and carbon.

IMPERMEABLE—Not permitting passage, impenetrable.

KEEL—The chief timber or steel piece extending along the entire length of the bottom of a vessel; generally, a boat's bottom.

KNOT—A unit of speed of one nautical mile (6,080.27 feet) per hour.

LOG, SHIP's—A written record of a ship's activities: course, speed, weather, and other information.

STARBOARD—To the right, facing forward, on a ship.

SUPERSTRUCTURE—That part of a ship above the main deck.

WAYS—The platform on which a ship is constructed and launched.

119

Index

(Page numbers in **boldface** are those on which illustrations appear.)

121

123